William Shakespeare

Julius Caesar

Retold by
Marcia Williams

WALKER
BOOKS

William Shakespeare

Julius Caesar

First published 2015 by Walker Books Ltd
87 Vauxhall Walk, London SE11 5HJ

2 4 6 8 10 9 7 5 3 1

This book has been typeset in Kennerly Regular

Printed and bound in Germany

British Library Cataloguing in Publication Data:
a catalogue record for this book is available from the British Library

ISBN 978-1-4063-6274-9

www.walker.co.uk

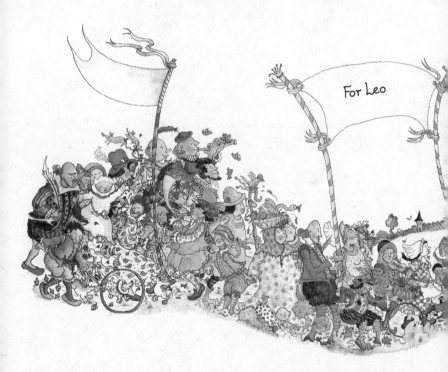

For Leo

Contents

In which Caesar
is humiliated.

It was a day of celebration and the streets of
ancient Rome swarmed with excited citizens
– cobblers, carpenters and tradespeople of
every kind. They were all dressed in their
finest clothes waiting to cheer their hero,
Julius Caesar, after a great victory over
his rival, Pompey. They brought flowers to
garland his statues, and petals and sweet-
smelling herbs to throw in his path.

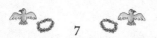

Two tribunes, Flavius and Marullus, tried
in vain to clear a way through the streets
and control the growing crowd's enthusiasm.
"Hence! Home, you idle creatures, get you
home," shouted Flavius. "Is this a holiday?"

The citizens' excitement angered Flavius
and Marullus, for it wasn't so long ago that

these people had cheered Pompey. At this
time, Rome was a republic – ruled by the
people through their senators. In the past,
Romans had fought to rid Rome of the rule
of bad and all-powerful monarchs. But now
some politicians feared Caesar wished to
become king. However, the common people

loved him, for he was a persuasive orator and great crowds always gathered to hear him speak.

"We make holiday to see Caesar, and to rejoice in his triumph!" they cried, undaunted by the tribunes' rising anger.

"You blocks, you stones, you worse than senseless things!" shouted Flavius and Marullus, waving their swords at the crowd.

All their efforts were in vain, for as the drums rolled and the trumpets sounded, Caesar appeared! A great cheer rose from the throng, making even the still waters of the River Tiber tremble. Dressed in purple and wearing the victor's laurel wreath, Caesar nodded and waved to the adoring crowd. Behind him walked the other greats of Rome, including two senators, Brutus and Cassius, and Caesar's friend Mark Antony, who was stripped and ready for the games. It was the Feast of Lupercal, when noblemen ran naked through the streets.

Suddenly the cheers and trumpets were silenced by a single, shrill call for Caesar.

"Ha! Who calls?" demanded Caesar.

An ancient soothsayer came out of the crowd and stood, bent and ragged, before

the great general. The crowd was hushed by his daring.

"Beware the Ides of March," he said, in a voice that echoed through the streets.

"He is a dreamer," scoffed Caesar. "Let us leave him."

The party moved off to watch the games, but many wondered what the soothsayer meant – the Ides of March was the fifteenth day of the month, which was not far off.

Brutus and Cassius hung back, for they

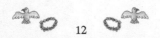

were not in the mood for games – they supported the republic and were sickened by Caesar's triumphant behaviour. They could hear the roar of the crowd as he took his seat for the games.

"What means this shouting?" sighed Brutus. "I do fear the people choose Caesar for their king."

"Ay, do you fear it?" replied Cassius. "Then must I think you would not have it so."

"I would not, Cassius," replied Brutus reluctantly. For though Brutus loved Caesar, he loved and honoured Rome more, and had no wish to see the return of a monarchy.

Later, the two men heard Caesar and his followers make their way back from the

games. Plainly things had not gone well for Caesar – he was looking grim. They called their friend, Casca, to one side.

"Would you speak with me?" Casca asked nervously.

"Tell us what hath chanced today, that Caesar looks so sad," said Brutus.

Casca looked about him, for these were dangerous times and he could not risk being caught making fun of Caesar. However, once

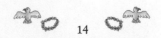

he saw that they were alone, Casca could
hardly contain his laughter as he recounted
how Mark Antony had offered Caesar the
crown. Caesar had refused it, hoping the
crowd would insist he accepted, but instead
the crowd had roared its approval! Three
times Mark Antony held up the crown and
three times the crowd roared and cheered
when Caesar refused it.

There was now no doubt in Brutus and
Cassius's minds that Caesar wished to be
king. Today they had been saved by the

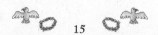

citizens, but who would save the republic tomorrow? Even noble Brutus began to consider what might be done, while Cassius's fingers twitched over his dagger.

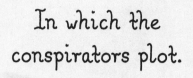

In which the conspirators plot.

That night there was a violent storm; it was as though the noise of some great battle hurtled through the skies. On the ground there were strange omens: horses screamed, dying men cried out and ghosts rose from their graves and walked wailing through the streets. It seemed the gods on Mount Olympus knew that Cassius, fearful that the Senate would offer Caesar the crown,

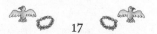

conspired to murder Caesar. He had already persuaded Decius, Cinna, Metellus Cimber, Trebonius and Casca to join him.

"I have moved already some certain of the noblest-minded Romans to undergo with me an enterprise," he mused.

"O Cassius! If you could but win the noble Brutus to our party," Cinna said.

Cassius knew Cinna was right. All Rome knew Brutus to be an honourable

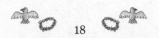

man, and his name would lend respect to
the deed. So Cassius, Cinna and the other
conspirators secretly made their way to
Brutus's house.

Although they made a strong case against
Caesar, Brutus was unwilling to join the
plot. He wanted what was best for Rome,
but it was a terrible thing to murder a friend.

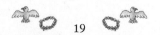

"Since Cassius first did whet me against Caesar," he said, "I have not slept."

As the sky roared angrily above them, the conspirators laid their plan before Brutus and finally convinced him. "Give me your hands all over, one by one," he said.

The assassination was planned for the following day, which happened to be the Ides of March. They resolved to kill Caesar in the Senate, before he could accept the

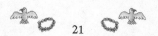

crown. "Let's kill him boldly, but not wrathfully," said Brutus, who sought to find some honour in the deed.

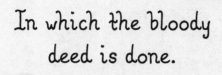

In which the bloody
deed is done.

In another part of Rome, Caesar's wife,
Calpurnia, was dreaming of his death.
Three times she cried out in her sleep, "Help,
ho! They murder Caesar." When morning
came, she begged Caesar to stay home and
not go to the Senate. She told him she had
had visions of his murder, and had seen
blood gush from his statues.

"Caesar shall go forth," he snapped. For

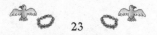

who, he thought, would dare to harm the great Caesar?

"Alas, my lord, your wisdom is consumed in confidence," cried Calpurnia, falling to her knees. "You shall not stir out of your house today."

But Caesar was tempted by the rumour that the Senate planned to offer him the crown. "How foolish do your fears seem. Give me my robe, for I will go!"

There was a knock at the door and the

senators Publius, Brutus, Ligarius, Metellus, Casca, Trebonius, Cinna and Mark Antony entered, ready to escort Caesar to the Senate. Through the streets they paraded, with Caesar in high spirits. He nodded and waved most regally to the early morning crowds, certain that by the evening he would wear the crown. Even when he met the soothsayer on the Senate steps, he was not upset.

"The Ides of March are come," he laughed.

"Aye Caesar; but not gone," came the chilling reply.

Inside the Senate, while Caesar listened to a petition, the conspirators slowly gathered round him, Cassius behind him and the others in front. Suddenly, without any warning, they all drew their daggers. Each one stabbed Caesar in turn. The last to stab Caesar was Brutus.

"Et tu, Brute?" cried Caesar. "Then fall, Caesar!"

"Liberty! Freedom! Tyranny is dead!" yelled Cinna. "Run hence, proclaim, cry it about the streets!"

As Caesar fell dead upon the floor, the other senators fled in fear and confusion.

"Fly not, stand still," shouted Brutus. "Ambition's debt is paid."

But they were gone. Only Mark Antony returned to grieve for his friend.

"Welcome, Mark Antony," said Brutus.

"O mighty Caesar! Dost thou lie so low?" cried Antony, falling to his knees beside Caesar's body. He turned to the conspirators and begged them to kill him too, if they bore him any grudge, but Brutus wanted no more bloodshed. He promised Antony that their

reasons for killing Caesar were justified.
"We will deliver you the cause why I, that
did love Caesar when I struck him, have
thus proceeded," he said.

Mark Antony asked if he could speak at Caesar's funeral as his friend and admirer and, against Cassius's advice, Brutus agreed.

"You know not what you do," said Cassius. "Do not consent." But it was too late.

Left alone with Caesar's lifeless body, Antony looked upon the bloody, open wounds and swore that he would avenge

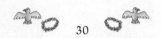

his friend's violent death. "Thou art the ruins of the noblest man that ever lived in the tide of times," he said, holding Caesar's body in his arms. "Woe to the hand that shed this costly blood!"

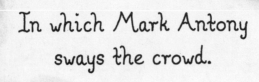

In which Mark Antony
sways the crowd.

News of Caesar's death spread like wildfire
through the city. By the time Brutus left
the Senate, an angry throng had gathered.

Their hero had been killed and now they wanted revenge. Brutus raised his hands for silence and the crowd was hushed.

"Romans, countrymen and lovers," he said. "As Caesar loved me, I weep for him; as he was valiant, I honour him: but, as he was ambitious, I slew him."

Brutus, with fine words and much passion, explained to Rome's shocked citizens that Caesar had threatened their freedom. He called for them to speak against him if they believed he had done wrong, but none did. A great cheer went up for Brutus and if he had not insisted that every citizen should stay to hear Mark Antony, he would have been carried home as their hero. As Brutus departed, Caesar's body was brought forth and laid upon a bier. Mark Antony began to speak. At first nobody would listen to him, but gradually the emotion in his voice silenced the crowd.

"Friends, Romans, countrymen, lend me your ears," he began. "I come to bury Caesar, not to praise him. The evil that men do lives after them; the good is oft interred with their bones."

Antony spoke of Caesar's great love for the people, and told the crowd he had left

money to each of them, and his gardens
and orchards to all. Then Antony lifted up
Caesar's mantle and showed the rapt citizens
the dagger marks. Everyone that watched
Antony could feel the wounds themselves,
so impassioned was his speech.

"O piteous spectacle!" cried one citizen.

"O noble Caesar!" cried another.

Mark Antony had succeeded – he had
turned the crowd against the conspirators.

Holding Caesar's body aloft like a trophy, the people swept through the streets, searching for his murderers, burning and looting as they went. With the citizens behind him, Antony knew he could drive out his enemies. "Now let it work: mischief, thou art afoot," he  whispered to himself. "Take thou what course thou wilt!"

Pursued by the angry mob, the conspirators were forced to flee the city, but they were determined to return. Over the

following months, Brutus and Cassius both raised armies, intending to retake Rome.

Meanwhile, Mark Antony formed an alliance with Octavius, Caesar's lawful heir. They too began to raise an army. To pay for

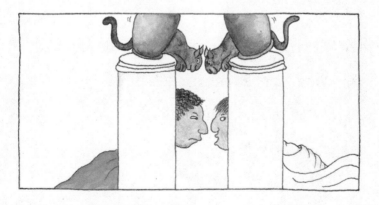

their legions, they stole the money Caesar had left the citizens of Rome.

In raising money for their armies, Brutus and Cassius quarrelled violently. Cassius had refused Brutus money for his army and had also defended a soldier who had taken bribes. Brutus's nobility was offended by these acts.

"Go to; you are not Cassius," he shouted.

"I am," replied his friend. "You love me not."

"I do not like your faults," Brutus declared.

"There is my dagger," said Cassius.

But Brutus had had enough. "Sheathe your dagger," he cried. "I am sick of many griefs." He confessed that his ill humour was caused by overwhelming sadness. His beloved wife, Portia, unable to bear being separated from him, had killed herself.

"O insupportable and touching loss!"
cried Cassius, forgetting his anger and
hugging his friend.

As Cassius comforted Brutus, news
arrived that Mark Antony and Octavius
were marching to Philippi with a powerful

army. This was not what Cassius and
Brutus had expected. They decided that
they would join forces with the remaining
conspirators and set out for Philippi to
confront their enemy, which was most

unwise and just what Antony hoped for.
He knew that the march was long and hard
and would exhaust the conspirators' legions
before the fighting even began.

In which the battle
for Rome is fought.

The night before the battle, while the
conspirators and their army was camped
outside Philippi, Brutus held out his hands
to Cassius. "If we do meet again, why, we
shall smile," he said. "If not, why then, this
parting is well made."

"For ever and for ever, farewell, Brutus!"
replied Cassius.

When the first pink rays of dawn broke,

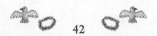

the drums rolled and the battle for Rome began. All day it raged: swords clashed and men and horses screamed. First it seemed one side was winning and then the other. However, as the day wore on, it was clear that Brutus and Cassius's armies, weakened by the long march to Philippi, were no match for the enemy – and as the sun set on their swords, they had to admit their defeat.

Cassius fell upon his own sword rather than witness the fall of the Roman Republic, along with many others who had not died

in battle. Many more fled – but as darkness fell and the eerie sound of the wounded and dying replaced the noise of battle, Brutus was still on the field. He lit a torch and held it aloft, searching amongst the wounded. Surely there must be one soldier left with the strength to hold his sword steady whilst he fell upon it? Brutus was weary and felt his bones were ready to rest.

Only one soldier stood ready to obey Brutus's last command.

"Hold then my sword, and turn away thy face while I do run upon it," Brutus ordered. "Caesar, now be still: I kill'd not thee with half so good a will."

So Brutus died swiftly and bravely. When Octavius and Antony heard that he was dead, Octavius was eager to celebrate their victory – but Antony paused. First he wanted to pay his respects to Brutus, whom he knew had been motivated to kill Caesar by neither greed nor envy, but by his love for Rome and its people.

WILLIAM SHAKESPEARE was a popular playwright, poet and actor who lived in Elizabethan England. He married in Stratford-upon-Avon aged eighteen and had three children, although one died in childhood. Shakespeare then moved to London, where he wrote 39 plays and over 150 sonnets, many of which are still very popular today. In fact, his plays are performed more often than those of any other playwright, and he died 450 years ago! His gravestone includes a curse against interfering with his burial place, possibly to deter people from opening it in search of unpublished manuscripts. It reads, "Blessed be the man that spares these stones, and cursed be he that moves my bones." Spooky!

MARCIA WILLIAMS' mother was a novelist and her father a playwright, so it's not surprising that Marcia ended up an author herself. Although she never trained formally as an artist, she found that motherhood, and the time she spent later as a nursery school teacher, inspired her to start writing and illustrating children's books.

Marcia's books bring to life some of the world's all-time favourite stories and some colourful historical characters. Her hilarious retellings and clever observations will have children laughing out loud and coming back for more!

More retellings from Marcia Williams

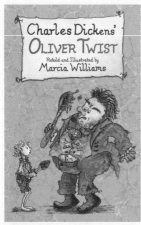

ISBN 978-1-4063-5692-2

ISBN 978-1-4063-5693-9

ISBN 978-1-4063-5694-6

ISBN 978-1-4063-5695-3

Available from all good booksellers

www.walker.co.uk